THE MATT MERTON
MYSTERIES

THE TRAP

Paul Blum

RISING ★ STARS

 nasen

NASEN House, 4/5 Amber Business Village, Amber Close,
Amington, Tamworth, Staffordshire B77 4RP

Rising Stars UK Ltd.
22 Grafton Street, London W1S 4EX
www.risingstars-uk.com

Text © Rising Stars UK Ltd.
The right of Paul Blum to be identified as the author of this work has
been asserted by him in accordance with the Copyright, Design and
Patents Act, 1988.

Published 2010

Cover design: pentacor**big**
Illustrator: Chris King, Illustration Ltd
Photos: Alamy
Text design and typesetting: pentacor**big/Clive Sutherland**
Publisher: Gill Budgell
Editorial consultants: Lorraine Petersen and Dee Reid

British Library Cataloguing in Publication Data.
A CIP record for this book is available from the British Library.

ISBN: 978-1-84680-797-8

Printed by Craft Print International Limited, Singapore

CONTENTS

THE CRASH

The Crash happened in 2021. Alien spaceships crash-landed on Earth. Now the aliens rule the world. They have changed shape so they look like people. People call the aliens The Enemy. Since The Crash, people are afraid. They don't know who is an Enemy and who is a friend.

An organisation called The Firm keeps order on the streets. The Firm keeps people safe from Enemy attacks — or do they?

People are going missing and the Earth is becoming colder and darker all the time. A new ice age is coming ...

ABOUT MATT MERTON

Matt Merton works for The Firm. He often works with **Dexter**. Their job is to find and kill The Enemy. They use Truth Sticks to do this.

But Matt has problems. He has lost some of his memory and cannot answer some big questions.

Where has **Jane**, his girlfriend, gone?

How did he get his job with **The Firm**?

Matt thinks The Firm is on the side of good. But he is not sure …

CHAPTER 1

Matt Merton's life was in danger. Matt had believed The Firm was protecting the world from aliens. Now he knew he was wrong. The Firm was working for the aliens. The people The Firm called 'The Enemy' were really the people who had been trying to stop the aliens.

Matt wanted to leave The Firm but he couldn't. The Firm were close to finding Jane. Matt needed to know why his missing girlfriend was so important to The Firm. He had to get to her first.

Matt also knew that Dexter, his partner in The Firm, was trying to kill him. He had tried twice before and failed.

Matt was sure he would not survive a third attack.

At The Firm they had a meeting.

'Dexter, what is your problem with Matt Merton?' asked the boss. 'Your orders were to let him lead us to Jane.'

'I don't trust him,' said Dexter. 'He's not on our side.'

'How do you know that?' asked the boss.

'He questions everything. He knows too much,' Dexter said. 'He is close to finding out everything.'

The boss was angry. 'Killing Merton is not your job. I give the orders. You will let him lead you to Jane. She is the target.'

'If he knows too much, he must be killed,' said a voice from the shadows. 'You have failed to do that twice.'

'We tried to kill him,' said Dexter. He could not see who was speaking.

'You did not try hard enough,' said the same voice. The boss said nothing.

'I did everything I could. Matt Merton is smart. He always survives,' said Dexter.

'You make excuses. I don't like excuses. I gave you a job to do and you failed.'

Two aliens dragged Dexter into the dark.

'Please, please, give me one more chance,' Dexter begged.

You have had your last chance,' the voice said. Dexter did not come back.

'Now I will find Matt Merton and kill him myself,' said the voice. 'When Merton is dead, I will find Jane and kill her too. She will not stop our plans. The world will soon be ours.'

CHAPTER 2

Matt stared at his mobile. He had a text from Jane. Matt had been looking for Jane for a long time. He couldn't believe she had made contact at last.

Matt felt so happy. Jane was alive and at last he would get answers. She could tell him why she had been hiding. He could find out why The Firm wanted her. They could work as a team to defeat the aliens at last.

Matt went out into the dark streets. It was a cold evening. Since The Crash, it was always winter. Every day the ice got thicker. A new ice age was on its way but all Matt could think about was seeing Jane again. He wanted to hear her voice, see her face and smell her perfume. He walked fast to the meeting place. He could see a woman. She stepped out of the shadows.

'Hello, Matt,' said Jane.

He felt overjoyed as he grabbed her hands.

'I've missed you so much,' he said. He hugged her. She seemed taller than he remembered. Taller, stronger and less shy. Her perfume had changed too. It wasn't the same as he remembered, but he had forgotten so much. He must be wrong.

'I've missed you too,' said Jane. Matt looked into her eyes. They didn't look the same. He started to feel worried.

'What have you been doing?' he asked. 'Where did you go on the night of The Crash? Why didn't you contact me? The Firm are looking for you too.'

He looked into her eyes but they were blank. It was as if she was a stranger. And why didn't she answer any of his questions?

'Come with me,' she said. 'You are in great danger.'

'I know,' he said. 'I think you are too.' He squeezed her hands. They seemed bigger.

Jane's whole body seemed bigger. Matt looked at her closely. She must have got fitter while she was in hiding. But how could she be taller? He shook his head. If only his memory wasn't so bad. If only he could remember more.

'The Firm will kill you,' said Jane. 'You know too much about their plans.'

'Do I?' said Matt. He smelt her perfume again — it was sour.

'Yes. You have seen their leader, ' she said.

'Have I?' he replied.

Matt wondered how Jane knew so much about what he had been doing recently. Had she been watching him? Had she talked to Sam in the cafe? No, Sam didn't know anything about his work. It was safer that way. Matt kept trying to work out what was wrong.

Jane could see he was confused. She smiled. It was a smile that changed her face. Her perfume had also changed. The air around Jane had become cold. Matt could smell salt water and rotting meat. He took a step backwards.

She started to change. Then Matt saw who she really was. It was not Jane. He had been led into a trap! The creature before him was no longer human. It grew in size until it became the thing that Matt had seen once before.

Jane had changed into the alien leader!

CHAPTER 3

'You cannot stop The Firm, Matt. We are growing stronger every day,' it said.

'We are taking over your world. There will be a new ice age. Only creatures that live deep below the sea will survive. There will be no need for weak humans. We will change the planet to serve our needs. All living things will be our slaves.'

Matt got out his Truth Stick but the alien snapped it in half.

'That stick is useless against me,' it said. 'It is just a toy I gave to people like you, Matt. You were good at using it to kill humans. But then you started finding out our secrets. Now we will find Jane without you. She cannot defeat us.'

The Truth Stick was broken. But as it broke, it made a shrill noise. The alien leader stopped speaking. It tried to grab Matt, but it did not like the noise. It began to shake. It couldn't move.

'Maybe the Truth Stick is more than just a toy after all,' shouted Matt. 'Maybe weak humans like the truth more than you do.'

Matt had gained a little time. He ran for his life. In a few seconds, the shrill noise from the Truth Stick would stop. The alien would be back to full strength and it would kill him.

Matt ran for a long time. He ran right across the city. Was he being followed? No. He slowed down. He felt so confused. Jane was the key to solving this puzzle. He had to hide from The Firm and try to find her. The alien had told him more of their plan. Now Matt just had to work out what to do next.

CHAPTER 4

Matt saw Sam's cafe. The lights were still on. He looked around. No one was following him. He went inside.

'You're open late,' said Matt.

'You're working late,' said Sam. 'Need a coffee?'

'Make it a big one,' said Matt. 'With all the extras.'

'You look like somebody just tried to kill you,' said Sam. 'How many times is that now?'

Matt nodded. 'Three times. The aliens trapped me. They are getting stronger.'

'Why won't you tell me about your work?' asked Sam.

'I don't want to put you in any danger,' said Matt.

'You can tell me anything,' said Sam. 'I'm your friend.'

'I know you are,' Matt said. 'That's why it is better that you know as little as possible.'

'It's time to lock up,' said Sam, changing the subject. He bolted the door.

'Sam, I need you to be very careful now,' said Matt. 'I can't say any more, but soon we may both have to go on the run.'

'Okay, Matt,' said Sam. 'I won't ask any more. But you know you can trust me.'

'I know I can. Thank you,' said Matt.

Matt and Sam sat in the dark. They were both scared but they felt safer in each other's company. For now...

QUIZ

1. How many time had Dexter tried to kill Matt?

2. What happened to Dexter during the meeting at The Firm?

3. Who sent a text to Matt?

4. What was different about Jane's hands?

5. What warning did Jane give Matt?

6. What happened to Jane?

7. What did the alien leader say would survive the new ice age?

8. What happened when the Truth Stick broke?

9. What did the noise do to the alien leader?

10. Why does Matt not want to tell Sam about his work?

GLOSSARY

defeat — to be beaten or to lose

excuses — reasons not to do something properly

key to solving the puzzle — person or thing that will provide the answer to a problem

made contact — got in touch with

perfume — a sweet-smelling liquid people wear

rotting — going stale

target — person who will be attacked

ANSWERS

1. Twice

2. He was dragged away and killed

3. Jane

4. They were bigger

5. The Firm would kill him as he knew too much about their plans

6. She changed into the alien leader

7. Creatures that live deep below the sea

8. It made a shrill noise

9. Make him shake and stop moving

10. Because it will put Sam in danger

CASE FILE

AUTHOR NAME
Paul Blum

JOB
Teacher

LAST KNOWN LOCATION
London, England

NOTES
Before The Crash taught in London schools. Author of *The Extraordinary Files* and *Shadows*. Believed to be in hiding from The Firm. Wanted for questioning. Seems to know more about the new ice age than he should ...

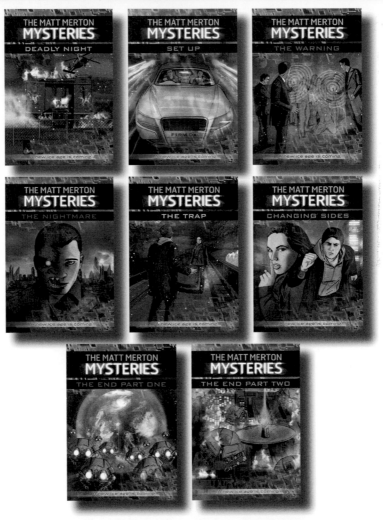